Lessons in
Learning to Learn

Understanding your amazing brain

Brain quiz – are these statements true or false?

1. Your brain has more than 100 billion neurons (brain cells).

2. You learn by making connections between these neurons.

3. All your neurons joined together would stretch from here to the moon.

4. Your brain needs plenty of oxygen and water to function properly.

5. If you don't use it, you lose it.

6. Your brain is the size of a large melon.

7. Your brain uses up 20% of your energy.

8. Learning makes your brain more powerful.

9. Your brain is more powerful than a computer the size of the Empire State Building.

10. If brain cells were trees in the Amazon rain forest and neural connections were the leaves, it would take 3 million years to count all the leaves.

A bee has 900 brain cells and a brain the size of a grain of salt

Now write a list of all the things a bee's brain has to think about to survive:

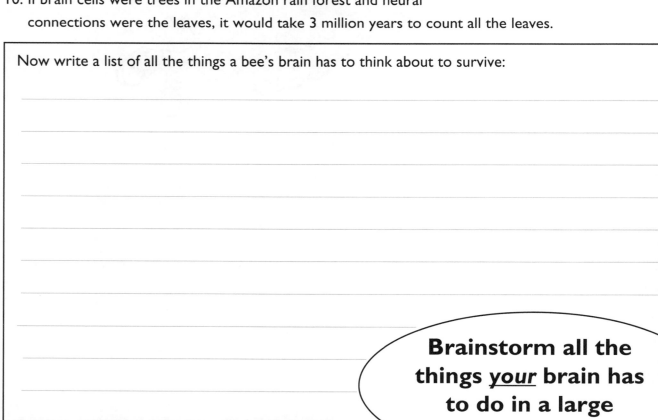

Brainstorm all the things _your_ brain has to do in a large learning map

Understanding your amazing brain

The things your brain has to do

Your P.E.T. brain

P is for Primitive – Reptilian brain

Primitive brain

Emotional brain

Thinking brain

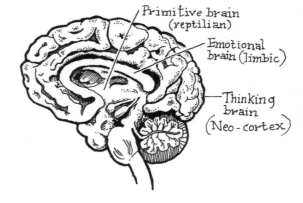

Your Primitive Brain – this keeps your body functioning and helps you survive. Sometimes it is called the reptilian brain because all reptiles have a brain with only this part well developed! If you are feeling threatened or stressed it 'kicks in' and can take over. Reptilian brain state can make you fight, freeze or want to run away.

Look at this example:

> Andy was on lesson report so he was working hard on his Maths. The teacher popped out of the room and just as she came back in a ruler went flying past her head. Andy looked up and she accused him of throwing it. He went reptilian. He shouted back at her, slammed his fist on the desk and got sent to the Head.

Discuss or write down an alternative reaction for Andy

What would **you** do …

- If a teacher picked on you unfairly?

- If you are challenged by your parents about using the phone or computer too much?

- If you saw someone small being bullied?

- If you saw the wing of the aeroplane you were travelling in was on fire?

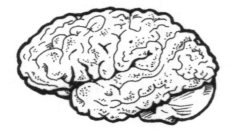

ROAD RAGE is an example of when adults go into reptilian brain state. What do you think happens and why?

Your P.E.T. brain

TASK 1

Think of 3 examples of situations when you or someone you know went 'reptilian'.

1. _____
2. _____
3. _____

TASK 2

You are being interviewed by police concerning an incident where you lost your temper.

Explain or write down your version of events.

_____
_____
_____
_____

WHAT TO DO IF YOU FEEL REPTILIAN?

1.   Write down here 3 ways to calm down and make a positive outcome more likely.

1. _____
2. _____
3. _____

2.   Write a set of slogans to say to yourself to control anger.

_____
_____
_____
_____

Your Emotional Brain

Your P.E.T. Brain – E is for Emotional brain

The limbic system

This part of your brain runs your emotions. It also stores memories and sets your values and beliefs. It is very important in learning. It's much easier to remember emotional experiences than facts. Try it.

- Recall your earliest childhood memory and share it with a partner.

- Now write down any nursery rhyme or songs you can remember from you childhood.

Your emotional brain loves praise, music, rhyme, colour, humour, novelty, enthusiasm and needs to see the point of learning.

- Which are your favourite lessons and teachers? Why?

- Can you link them to your emotional brain?

Many famous sport stars train in their 'heads', visualising superb performance make it happen.

Learning is emotional...

1. Make it exciting, colourful, funny, and musical. Think of ways to do this with tests coming up ... *now*.

2. Give yourself a reason for learning. As long as *you* care, it will count.

3. Set yourself goals for learning and reward your efforts.

4. Use your imagination to help you become a better learner.

5. Use your imagination to help you be more successful at sport or when performing.

How can you use your emotional brain to help you learn?

TASK

Write your success story *now*. Describe a day in your life when everything goes brilliantly and you are a superstar – especially at learning. Start like this:
'I woke up and the sun was shining. I felt great about the day ahead because...

It doesn't matter if your story seems unlikely or impossible. The more extreme you make it the better!

Now act out your day in groups of 3 or 4.

Your Emotional Brain

My success story

_____

_____

_____

_____

_____

_____

_____

_____

_____

_____

_____

_____

_____

_____

_____

_____

_____

_____

_____

_____

The Thinking Brain

Your P.E.T. Brain – T is for Thinking brain

This is your 'thinking cap' where all the hard work takes place. The brain is sometimes thought of as divided into hemispheres which deal with different things.

Two Halves Make You Whole

LOGICAL (left)

Writing
Logic
Numbers
Analysing
Reading
Sequencing
Language
Detail
Spelling

CREATIVE (right)

Ideas
Intuition
Daydreams
Sport
Playing music
The big picture
Rhythm
Colour
Imagination

These different ways of thinking need to work together to make best use of our brains. For example, when we are doing a jigsaw puzzle we sort out the pieces using colour and shape, but we also have to think about the 'big picture' and imagine how it all fits together to get it right.

To help understand the way your brain works – answer these questions:

Yes or No.

Score: Yes _____ /10

No _____ /10

More Yes than No?
You may be more of a
left-brain thinker.

1. I organise facts and material well	Yes ☐	No ☐
2. I work step by step	Yes ☐	No ☐
3. I can be impatient	Yes ☐	No ☐
4. I read instructions before starting	Yes ☐	No ☐
5. I like to work things out on paper	Yes ☐	No ☐
6. I like working on my own	Yes ☐	No ☐
7. I like to make lists	Yes ☐	No ☐
8. I can concentrate well	Yes ☐	No ☐
9. I like reading	Yes ☐	No ☐
10. I enjoy working with numbers	Yes ☐	No ☐

The Thinking Brain

Now answer these questions Yes or No.

Score: Yes _____ /10

No _____ /10

11. I prefer variety and excitement   Yes ☐   No ☐

12. I like to doodle a lot   Yes ☐   No ☐

13. I love trying new ideas   Yes ☐   No ☐

> More Yes than No?
> You may be more of a
> right-brain thinker.

14. I think of creative solutions   Yes ☐   No ☐

15. I like new experiences   Yes ☐   No ☐

16. I just try out ideas as I go along   Yes ☐   No ☐

17. I prefer to flick through a magazine starting at the back   Yes ☐   No ☐

18. I make decisions based on gut feelings   Yes ☐   No ☐

19. I find it hard to concentrate quite often   Yes ☐   No ☐

20. I prefer art to reading and maths   Yes ☐   No ☐

> If you have a fairly equal number of yes/no answers you are in the middle, which is an excellent place to be because you are using both sides of your brain for learning!

Learning health check

Using ALL of your brain can make you more clever, so once you know which way you tend to think watch out for these health warnings …

Tips for Left brainers:

● You may need to be more open to trying new approaches.

● Don't get bogged down in detail.

● Practise working well with others.

● Vary your learning styles and habits to keep your creative brain working.

Tips for Right brainers:

● Remember the details – one step at a time.

● Make yourself do some planning and prioritising in advance.

● Avoid procrastination (putting things off!).

● Avoid distraction and distracting others.

● Don't rush in without thinking.

● Read the instructions and check your work when finished.

Get into the habit of using your right and left-brain during learning.
This will make you very intelligent!

● How could you use more right-brain thinking in maths?

● How could you use more left-brain thinking in drama or art?

TASK

● Fill in the two halves of a brain diagram with different activities in right and left hemispheres.

The Thinking Brain

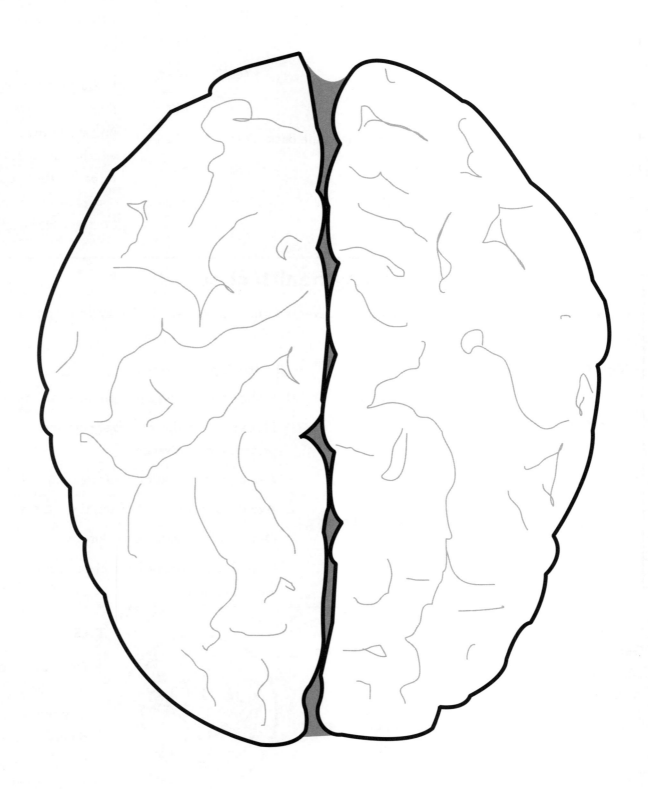

Brain Boosters

Warm up for Learning

The brain works best when the two sides, left and right, work together. Here are some ways of getting the left brain and right brain working well to warm up for learning!

- Stand up, stretch, reach up and breathe deeply to give your brain oxygen.

- Rub your tummy with one hand, pat your head with the other.

- Do the twist – arms one way, legs the other way.

- Lift your knee and touch it with the opposite hand. Alternate quickly.

- Draw a large figure of eight in the air with one finger. Draw another large figure eight with the other finger going the other way – make sure your fingers don't touch!

- Trace out the number 10, in the air with one hand creating the 1 and the other hand. Try it with 27, 39 and your age.

- With one hand trace a circle moving outwards from your body. Use the other hand to trace a circle inwards towards your body. Keep them both going at the same time.

- Put your fingertips together very lightly and imagine connections being made between the right and left sides of your brain.

- Fold your arms one way then the other way – repeat until it feels comfortable each way.

- Make your hands into fists and put these together to form a shape that resembles your brain. Blow some energy and power into the gap between your thumbs.

In the air or on paper:

- Write your full name with your wrong hand in large letters.

- Write your name with both hands, creating a mirror image.

- Try writing your name backwards with your wrong hand.

- Write your favourite band, country, and food – using your wrong hand.

- Create an impressive signature then copy with your wrong hand.

- Throw your pen from one hand to the other and back again.

Boost your brain by trying something new every day. A food you don't eat, a TV programme you never watch, a person you don't usually speak to – make new connections!

Brain Boosters

Warm up for Learning

The brain works best when the two sides, left and right, work together. Here are some ways of getting the left brain and right brain working well to warm up for learning!

- Stand up, stretch, reach up and breathe deeply to give your brain oxygen.

- Rub your tummy with one hand, pat your head with the other.

- Do the twist – arms one way, legs the other way.

- Lift your knee and touch it with the opposite hand. Alternate quickly.

- Draw a large figure of eight in the air with one finger. Draw another large figure eight with the other finger going the other way – make sure your fingers don't touch!

- Trace out the number 10, in the air with one hand creating the 1 and the other hand. Try it with 27, 39 and your age.

- With one hand trace a circle moving outwards from your body. Use the other hand to trace a circle inwards towards your body. Keep them both going at the same time.

- Put your fingertips together very lightly and imagine connections being made between the right and left sides of your brain.

- Fold your arms one way then the other way – repeat until it feels comfortable each way.

- Make your hands into fists and put these together to form a shape that resembles your brain. Blow some energy and power into the gap between your thumbs.

In the air or on paper:

- Write your full name with your wrong hand in large letters.

- Write your name with both hands, creating a mirror image.

- Try writing your name backwards with your wrong hand.

- Write your favourite band, country, and food – using your wrong hand.

- Create an impressive signature then copy with your wrong hand.

- Throw your pen from one hand to the other and back again.

Boost your brain by trying something new every day. A food you don't eat, a TV programme you never watch, a person you don't usually speak to – make new connections!

Brain Boosters

Warm up for Learning

The brain works best when the two sides, left and right, work together. Here are some ways of getting the left brain and right brain working well to warm up for learning!

- Stand up, stretch, reach up and breathe deeply to give your brain oxygen.

- Rub your tummy with one hand, pat your head with the other.

- Do the twist – arms one way, legs the other way.

- Lift your knee and touch it with the opposite hand. Alternate quickly.

- Draw a large figure of eight in the air with one finger. Draw another large figure eight with the other finger going the other way – make sure your fingers don't touch!

- Trace out the number 10, in the air with one hand creating the 1 and the other hand. Try it with 27, 39 and your age.

- With one hand trace a circle moving outwards from your body. Use the other hand to trace a circle inwards towards your body. Keep them both going at the same time.

- Put your fingertips together very lightly and imagine connections being made between the right and left sides of your brain.

- Fold your arms one way then the other way – repeat until it feels comfortable each way.

- Make your hands into fists and put these together to form a shape that resembles your brain. Blow some energy and power into the gap between your thumbs.

In the air or on paper:

- Write your full name with your wrong hand in large letters.

- Write your name with both hands, creating a mirror image.

- Try writing your name backwards with your wrong hand.

- Write your favourite band, country, and food – using your wrong hand.

- Create an impressive signature then copy with your wrong hand.

- Throw your pen from one hand to the other and back again.

Boost your brain by trying something new every day. A food you don't eat, a TV programme you never watch, a person you don't usually speak to – make new connections!

Brain Boosters

Have a brain/body work out

Imagine that you are at the gym and a huge set of weights is in front of you. IN YOUR MIND, see yourself in full gym kit looking strong and happy bending your knees and picking up the weights. See yourself lift the weights slowly, keeping your back straight. Then raise the weights to your shoulders. Feel the weight, feel your strength. When you are steady lift them above your head and straighten your arms. Feel the weight for a few seconds then place carefully lower them back to your shoulders. Do this ten times then place them carefully back on the floor. This mental exercise can make you stronger in the real world. ('Mind Sculpture' Robertson 1999.)

Review: Your Amazing Brain

Write down five things you have learnt in Section 2:1, Amazing Brains (Lessons 24–30)

1. _____

2. _____

3. _____

4. _____

5. _____

Write down three action points for you from this section.

1. _____

2. _____

3. _____

Share these ideas with a partner. Put this sheet on your bedroom wall.

See Sense

How to use your senses for learning

We experience everything we learn through our five senses.

Seeing, Hearing, Touching, Tasting, Smelling

Can you think of anything you experienced that didn't involve the senses?

How did your last lesson smell??

First thoughts

Dogs use their sense of smell to decide who they like and who is a threat.
Think of five ways in which dogs demonstrate their powerful sense of smell.

Blind people show a remarkable development in their other senses.
How can blind people use other senses to 'see'?

We have already discovered that our brains are like our fingerprints – they are all different.
Our multiple intelligences show how we all have different skills and strengths.
This is because we all learn in different ways.

As adults we mainly use three senses for learning – see, hear and touch but we tend to have a preference for learning using one of the three senses.

Preferred learning styles

VISUAL   prefer to learn by seeing, looking at pictures …

AUDITORY   prefer to learn by listening to sounds, going to lectures, taking part in discussions …

KINESTHETIC   prefer to learn by 'hands-on' experience, engaging physically with the world …

You need to know if *you* have a learning preference because it can affect your success if you depend too much on one learning sense. Your challenge is to be good at using all three for learning.

See Sense

Tick which of these apply to you:

VISUAL LEARNERS	AUDITORY LEARNERS	KINESTHETIC LEARNERS
● Have a neat and tidy workplace ☐	● Talk to themselves ☐	● Like physical activity ☐
● Have good presentation skills ☐	● Tell jokes ☐	● Like to make things ☐
● Plan ahead ☐	● Like speeches and singing out loud ☐	● Use gestures ☐
● Like to look good ☐	● Prefer verbal instructions ☐	● Fidget and find it hard to sit still ☐
● Enjoy pictures and maps ☐	● Are distracted by noise ☐	● Need to *do* things to remember them ☐
● Don't always listen well ☐	● Listen well ☐	● Enjoy sport, drama, dance ☐
● Daydream a lot ☐	● Enjoy rhyme/ rhythm ☐	● Like action and action words ☐
● Draw, scribble and doodle ☐	● Discuss and argue well ☐	● Say 'I'll handle that' ☐
● Say 'I see what you mean' ☐	● Say 'Sounds great to me' ☐	● Are easily distracted ☐
TOTAL /9	/9	/9

See Sense

Now check out your sensory preference using this questionnaire:

Tick which of the alternatives below applies most closely to your preference for learning.

Add the scores from page 112 to these.

I like:	SEEING Visual		HEARING Auditory		DOING Kinesthetic	
To learn through:	pictures/diagrams/ video		listening to teachers, tapes or people speaking		practical activity	
To spell by:	seeing the word in my mind		sounding out the letters		writing the word out a number of times	
To relax through:	watching TV, sport or films		listening to music or the radio		playing games or sport	
To learn a foreign language through:	looking at cards, posters, videos and books		listening to tapes and saying the words		playing games and role-plays	
To learn a new sport by:	watching a demonstration		listening to instructions and talking to a coach		playing it	
To learn in science by:	looking at diagrams in books and teacher demonstrations		listening to a teacher talking		doing practical experiments	
To remember events by:	seeing images, scenes, faces and colours		hearing sounds, words or music		focusing on action and feelings about the event	
To write:	descriptive passages		speech and dialogue		action stories	
To find out information by:	looking in books		asking an expert and listening to them		surfing the worldwide web	
Which describes you best?	I like to plan ahead and see the future		I sometimes talk or sing to myself		I get restless if I sit still for too long	
TOTAL SCORES IN EACH COLUMN:		/10		/10		/10
OVERALL SCORE	V	/19	A	/19	K	/19

Are you an auditory, visual or kinesthetic learner?

We all use all of our senses so many of you will be balanced between two or all three categories.

Use as many senses as possible to make learning more memorable.

Lesson 32

Be a powerful visual learner

Use your eyes to see and use your mind to create visual pictures

You have discovered you learning sensory preference. But the best learners use *all* their senses to learn. Whatever your preference for learning you need to develop *each* of your senses for powerful learning.

First thoughts

Imagine a cat sitting on your lap. See yourself stroking it, see its colour and feel its texture. What colour is the cat?

If you find it hard to visualise the cat, then you need to practise using internal visualising for learning!

Learning maps

Creating a learning map involves writing down all the important information you need to know but writing it down in a way that is brain friendly and that captures your visual imagination. Most of the time we write our notes in lists and paragraphs. This does not always help us remember them. Good learning maps use:

COLOUR

PICTURES

SYMBOLS AND IMAGES

WORDS

These are all brain friendly and give us visual stimulation.

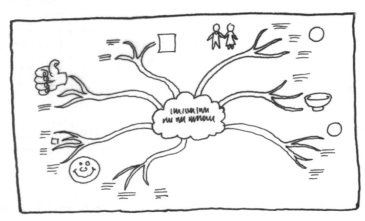

Be a powerful visual learner

Learning maps start with a central idea and grow branches in all directions as ideas flow. It doesn't matter if they are not artistic or organised.

Start this learning map on yourself. Start in the middle of the sheet of paper with the key word you are going to use to grow your ideas from. Draw a box containing the word 'ME' and then add – radiating out from this central point – where you live, what type of house, people in your family, pets, your personality, your hobbies and so on.

It doesn't matter how untidy it is – just get as much information down as you can. You can always redraw it later when themes and patterns emerge – and this will assist your learning. Don't put any pictures in this map.

Here are some simple drawings – what does each one mean to you? Draw a learning map for each one.

Be a powerful visual learner

Pictures can be simple and easy to draw. You need to use simple pictures and images in your learning maps – but you don't have to be an artist.

Make a pictorial learning map

Now on a larger piece of paper convert your learning map about yourself into a map made entirely of colourful symbols, pictures, cartoons and diagrams. They can be as simple and silly as you like.

Add the words from your first map after you have finished all the pictures.

Add a title – **now you have a learning map with words and pictures that is easy to learn from.**

Give it to a neighbour to study for 5 minutes – then test how much they have learnt about you.

Ask them how they remembered bits of the map. Was it through the pictures or the words? Did they see the map inside their heads? If they did they were using their visual memory.

Now create a learning map for a science topic or for a book you are studying. Remember to use lots of key words, colours and pictures.

It is *your* learning map, so it doesn't matter if it isn't neat or tidy as long as **you** understand it.

From now on:

Look in on your internal visual learning cinema. Spend time enjoying daydreaming, reliving happy times and rerunning good lessons that helped you learn.

Also,

- Ask your teachers if you can map your notes in your book if that helps you to learn. Visual, right brain learners learn better from mind maps.

- Use learning maps to revise for tests.

- Use learning maps to plan and organise yourself.

- Try mapping on the computer using www.mindman.com.

Be a powerful visual learner

Your learning map

Using your inner eye

The cinema screen that is your mind

First thoughts

Do you remember in words or pictures?

Developing your visual learning involves being able to create pictures in your mind and then using them to help you learn.

- Imagine a puppy sitting on the desk in front of you

- Write down exactly what it looks like and what it is doing. See yourself playing with it and picking it up.

- Now change the puppy into a snake. Does this feel different?

Imagining things can make you feel physical effects!

These visual memories are very important in learning. Try some mental arithmetic – do you see it in your head?

In pairs:

How good is your inner eye?

Describe the walls of this classroom without looking at them.

Recall your last lesson – describe in as much detail what you can see in your mind.

Each pair give a mark out of ten for the amount their partner can remember.

Now recall the best lesson/experience you ever had – make the picture in your head bright and colourful and as big as a cinema screen.
Describe it to each other in pairs.
How does it make you feel to see it in your head?
Draw a spider diagram/doodle of that lesson with images and words that capture the atmosphere.

Spell out a word – do you see it first?

TASK

1. Put some lively, familiar music on. Write down or draw all the visual images that come into your head.

2. Write a paragraph about how visualising in your head helps **you** to learn.

Using your inner eye

Did you know your eyes move when you are visualising something in your head?

The moving eye test

Look straight at a partner and ask these questions. Fill in which direction the eyes move for each answer.

What colour is your front door?

Imagine seeing a purple lion.

How many people and animals live at your house?

What would I look like with blue hair?

What would an elephant squeaking sound like?

Think of your favourite song and listen to it in your head.

Your eyes move to a different place when they look in your head for information or try to imagine something. Make up four more questions to test out eye movement.

Create your own virtual reality

Give your visual imagination a workout every day by daydreaming a situation where you are the hero of a success story.

Try it now – put some soft music on and set the scene in your head. This works even better if you do the relaxation exercise first. (Lesson 13)

Now draw a picture **or** write an account of this story to remind yourself.

Tips for visual learning

● Put posters, charts, key words and your learning maps on your bedroom wall.

● Use lots of colour, and highlighter pens in your notes, especially for key words and concepts.

● Watch videos, read books – especially illustrated books. Use interactive software or the internet to help you learn.

● Develop your listening skills and make sure you take part in any practical activities. Don't just sit and watch!

● Take some time out to regularly visualise and rerun all your best lessons and best moments. Do this just before you go to sleep for maximum impact!

Improve literacy through visualisation

Turn movies on in your head when you read

'Man's mind cannot understand thoughts without images of them' *Thomas Aquinas*

Visualising for comprehension

If you can make pictures in your mind it can help you understand what you read and this will help you in exams.

Read this passage from 'Unforgettable places to see before you die' by Steve Davey.

1. As you stand in the cold darkness of an Arizona night, waiting for dawn, you will have no comprehension of the enormity of the landscape in front of you. In the dull early light your first view of the Grand Canyon will be a flat, almost painterly composition.

2. Then gradually the sky turns to blue and red, and golden sunlight starts to pick out details – first the edge of the far ridge, then the tallest pinnacles inside the canyon itself.

3. As the sun rises higher, more is revealed. Rock formations sculpted by years of erosion are illuminated, and long, convoluted shadows are cast on to giant screens formed by cliffs.

4. Only when you notice the details, such as a row of trees, or a flock of geese flying overhead, do you come to realise the true scale of the canyon. That far ridge might be 15km away, and the mighty Colorado River – a mere stream viewed from above – is 1500 metres below.

Improve literacy through visualisation

For each section 1–4

Create a picture in your head.

In each box either write words or draw pictures or stick men to show what is in these pictures.

Add extra details that make it more interesting but still fits with the text.

Describe in words what is in each picture to your neighbour.

1	2

3	4

Improve literacy through visualisation

Test how this has improved your memory and understanding by describing what is in the passage below.

Make it into a film.

Making visual images can help you understand and remember poetry.

Create a picture for each section of this famous speech in Shakespeare's 'Macbeth'.

1. 'Tomorrow and tomorrow and tomorrow
   Creeps in this petty pace from day to day
   To the last syllable of recorded time

2. And all our yesterdays have lighted fools the
   way to dusty death. Out, out brief candle!
   Life's but a walking shadow, a poor player
   That struts and frets his hour upon the stage
   And then is heard no more;

3. It is a tale
   Told by an idiot, full of sound and fury
   Signifying nothing'

Describe to your neighbour what is in each picture and why.

See how much of the poem and its meaning you can now remember.

The more you practise visualising and talking about those pictures the easier you will find it to remember things and understand meanings.

1

2

3

The best learners are listeners!

Learn with your ears – auditory learning

Some people learn well through listening. Listening is a very important skill to acquire as so much of what we have to learn is presented auditorily by teachers talking to the group, or through group discussions. Therefore, every student needs to have good **listening skills**.

Listen to the sounds around you now – jot down everything you can hear.

Auditory learners say:

Can you hear what I am saying?

That rings a bell with me.

I've heard it all before.

Now listen to your insides – what can you hear?

What makes a good listener?

The best learners are listeners!

How do you know you have heard something?

What mental processes go on after you have heard something important?

In pairs, find out how good you are at listening. Here are some activities that will involve careful listening:

- Listen to a poem read out by the teacher – once. See how many words and phrases from the poem you can remember and jot them down.

- Tell your partner some details of your last holiday – make them repeat back to you the main points.

- Play a piece of music or a pop song and really listen to the words and music. Try singing it afterwards.

Listening skills are vital to learning and to life.

TASK – in pairs

Imagine you are at a counselling session. One of you is the counsellor, one the client. Tell the counsellor your real (or imaginary) problems about school or home in three or four minutes. The counsellor then has to repeat back to you a summary of the problems and suggest some solutions.

We listen in our heads too!

Listen to your internal dialogue – you know the voice that talks to you inside your head. It often gives you a running commentary on what you are doing and what you are going to do. What sort of voice is it? Is it your voice? Change the way it sounds. If it is normally miserable and complaining then make it positive and encouraging. This can be very motivating. How does this change make you feel? What did your inner voice just say? Was it positive?

The best learners are listeners!

My business card

The best learners are listeners!

Look at this example:

You are asked to do a bungee jump for charity. Two thoughts that may come into your head are:

Internal voice: 'I might die! People get injured. I might chicken out at the last minute and look like a fool.'

Positive voice: 'That could be exciting. I can do it and think how good it would make me feel. I will be making money for someone else.'

Which one is closer to how **you** think?

Practise now making your internal voice say something positive to you.

Make the most of self-talk to build confidence and self belief

AVOID – Negative self-talk

I can't do it.
She hates me.
I've never been good at exams.
My writing is rubbish.
No one likes me.
It's bound to go wrong.
Add some more.

INCREASE – Positive self-talk

I'm brilliant and beautiful!
I can do anything if I work hard enough.
I love exams.
I am an excellent friend.
I am very determined to get it right.
I am born lucky.
Add some more.

TASK

Create a business card with all your positive self-talk statements on it to remind you how to help build your confidence.

Tips for auditory learning:

- Read your notes out loud.
- Make a cassette tape of your notes.
- Make your notes into a rhyme or rap – or even better, sing them!
- Talk out loud to yourself when you are trying to understand something.
- Listen to music while you are working.

- Spell out words by making the sounds out loud.
- Teach other people what you know.
- Listen to your inner voice. Teach it to say positive things about you and about what you are doing.

Kinesthetic Learning

I can handle that!

Some people learn best by practical activity. Everyone benefits from reinforcing learning by practical activity.

Kinesthetic learners prefer to get on and do things rather than listen to instructions or watch the video.

Although kinesthetic learners find it hard to sit still, they still need to learn through the other senses too. Practise listening and meditating to become an all-round learner.

If you are not inclined towards kinesthetic learning you need to make sure you grab every opportunity for practical activity because this way your brain will keep developing.

Practical exercises do help you learn something more thoroughly.

Role-play helps you learn by doing.

Learn French through role-play

Make up a play using as many of these twelve French words as possible. You can only speak French and the rest of the play must be mimed.

bonjour (hello)	bien (well/good)	chien (dog)
chat (cat)	manger (eat)	maison (house)
eau (water)	au revoir (goodbye)	s'il vous plait (please)
jambon (ham)	fromage (cheese)	jus d'orange (orange juice)

Now test your knowledge of the French vocabulary.

Use cards to help you learn.

Brainstorm in any order the key events and characters from a film or book you have seen or read recently. Write each one on small cards or Post-its™. Organise each card on your desk in the correct order and move them into a pattern you like. Then talk through them to a neighbour.

Now do this again, this time choosing a science topic. For example, the characteristics of living things. Make the key cards and arrange them in the order that makes sense. This way you will learn more effectively than just reading your notes. Try it with a maths method or a food recipe.

Kinesthetic Learning

Try to do some of these kinesthetic activities every week

Dancing	Juggling
All sports, games and the gym	Arts and craft
Pottery	Cooking
Swimming	Cycling
Drama	Gardening

Kinesthetic learning creates a mind-body connection that can help you remember things.

TIPS FOR KINESTHETIC LEARNING

- Make a model of the process.
- Role-play what you have learnt.
- Do regular brain boosters (Lesson 30).
- Go on field trips and visits to enhance learning.
- Use Post-its™ notes to write and draw on.
- Use fingers to count on.
- Doodle while listening.
- Use a stress ball to squeeze.

Be active in your learning. Always volunteer an answer to questions and get involved in the lessons.

Review of MULTISENSORY LEARNING.

Write down five things you have learnt from this section:

1. _____
2. _____
3. _____
4. _____
5. _____

Write down three targets for improving your learning through all your senses.

1. _____
2. _____
3. _____

How can I be a genius?

There are lots of ways to be clever

Find out in this section how you are clever in many different ways and how you can use this to improve results.

First thoughts:

What is intelligence?

Name some famous geniuses

What things do very intelligent people do and say?

Neuroscientists now think that intelligence isn't just being good at Maths or English but that there are many different ways to be intelligent.

You have…Multiple Intelligences!

There are lots of ways you are smart. Here are some of them:

Discuss each one with a friend and decide which apply most to you.

Interpersonal   or   People smart

Are you good at getting on with people – not just your friends but adults, children, teachers? Are you a good listener, showing consideration and tolerance? Do you work well in groups and enjoy meeting new people? Are you generally popular with friends? People smart means you are skilful at getting on with others – you have to have interpersonal intelligence to do this.

Intrapersonal   or   Self smart

Understanding yourself and the way you work is vital for success in life. Intrapersonal intelligence is about being aware of your feelings and understanding your strengths and weaknesses. Can you control your moods and motivate yourself? Can you explain the way you behave in certain situations? Are you good at setting yourself targets and sticking to promises? If you are then you have a high intrapersonal intelligence.

How can I be a genius?

Linguistic   or   Word smart

If you enjoy reading and talking using a well developed vocabulary you will be word smart. You may be good at writing essays and stories and enjoy playing around with words and meanings. If you are word smart your favourite lesson may be English.

Mathematical and Logical   or   Number smart

Are you good at solving problems and sorting things out in a step by step fashion? Do you make lists of things to do and work through them? Your favourite subjects may be maths and science and you enjoy brainteasers and puzzles. If this sounds like you – you are number smart.

Visual and Spatial   or   Picture smart

Do you think in pictures? If you enjoy drawing, painting and looking at pictures, these are signs of visual/spatial intelligence. Learning more effectively from maps, graphs and pictures is easy for picture smart people.

Physical and Kinesthetic   or   Body smart

This is the ability to use your body skilfully in sport, dance or in building and constructing things. If you are strong in this intelligence you will enjoy lessons like PE, drama and technology. You will enjoy doing things yourself rather than watching others and will sometimes find it hard to sit still!

Musical   or   Music smart

If you have got good rhythm and enjoy singing or playing an instrument you are likely to have a strong musical intelligence. Do you listen to a variety of music because you want to and can you pick out patterns and instruments that others don't seem to notice? This is another sign of being music smart.

How can I be a genius?

Naturalist   **or**   **Nature smart**

If you are nature smart then you are aware and interested in all plants and animals, insects and rocks and the relationship between them. You may love being outdoors and care about the environment around you. You may be very aware of animal rights issues and hope to have a career in an outdoor environment.

TASK 1

Think of an activity you do that uses each intelligence.

People	Self	Word	Number	Picture	Body	Music	Nature

TASK 2

In groups of 4/5 create a role-play that shows the different intelligences at work in the brain. You can imagine the brain as a huge machine, with the different parts represented by movements or people. Try switching parts off and on. Show your role-play to the group.

How can I be a genius?

How am I smart?

The intelligences I use

First thoughts

Guess which you think your top 3 Smarts are and write them here:

_____

_____

Now you may have an idea of which intelligences are your strengths and maybe which are those you need to work on. Complete this questionnaire to check out your scores.

Score yourself with 1–5 marks for each question – 5 being high. Be honest!

1. I am good at working with objects and making things. ☐
2. I am good at finding my way around. ☐
3. I am good at sorting out arguments with friends. ☐
4. I can remember words to songs easily. ☐
5. I always do things one step at a time. ☐
6. I know myself well and understand why I behave the way I do. ☐
7. I keep/like pets and other animals. ☐
8. I enjoy socialising with friends. ☐
9. I learn well from talks and listening to people. ☐
10. When I listen to music it can change my mood. ☐
11. I can explain things clearly to people. ☐
12. I enjoy puzzles, crosswords and logic problems. ☐

How am I smart?

13.   I learn a lot from pictures, posters and diagrams.

14.   I am sensitive to the moods and feelings of those around me.

15.   I learn best when I get up and do it for myself.

16.   I prefer to be outside in the open air whenever I can.

17.   I learn best when I have set myself a goal.

18.   I enjoy peace and quiet for working.

19.   When listening to music I can recognise different instruments.

20.   I get angry when animals are maltreated or the environment is abused.

21.   I can picture places and faces easily in my head.

22.   I know a good range of words and I like to learn new ones.

23.   I enjoy writing.

24.   I have a good sense of balance and enjoy dancing.

25.   I can understand graphs and use a calculator properly.

26.   I work well in a team or group.

27.   I am observant and often see things others don't.

28.   I get restless and fidgety easily.

29.   I enjoy working on a project by myself.

30.   I can recognise different types of birds, trees or plants.

31.   I enjoy making music.

32.   I am good with numbers and maths.

How am I smart?

Scoring your answers

Intelligence		Score for each question								Total
Interpersonal	People Smart	3	8	14	26					
Intrapersonal	Self Smart	6	17	18	29					
Linguistic	Word smart	9	11	22	23					
Maths/logical	Number smart	5	12	25	32					
Visual/spatial	Picture Smart	2	13	21	27					
Kinesthetic	Body Smart	1	15	24	28					
Musical	Music Smart	4	10	19	31					
Naturalist	Nature Smart	7	16	20	30					

Now fill in the intelligence graph below to see how your scores compare.

	people	self	word	number	picture	body	music	nature
20								
15								
10								
5								

Take control ...

Why are your scores like this? _____

_____

_____

What do you need to do to improve your low scores?

_____

_____

_____

Using all your intelligences

To become a genius you need to work on all your intelligences

Look at your multiple intelligence graph again. Remember:

To become a genius you need to work on ALL your intelligences.

Fill in this chart of things to do to improve each intelligence.

People Smart	Self Smart	Word Smart	Number Smart	Picture Smart	Body Smart	Music Smart	Nature Smart
Listen to others	Think more often!	Learn a new word every day	Practise mental arithmetic and tables	Do jigsaws	Learn to juggle	Play music while you work	Plant something and watch it grow
Smile	Keep a diary	Read more	Do puzzle books	Develop your doodling skills	Learn a dance routine	Sing in the shower	Collect some leaves

TASK

In groups of four using a large piece of paper, plan a weekend away for a group of students. Make a programme of activities that will use all their multiple intelligences and improve them. Make it visual. Use pictures, flow charts or diagrams to show the activities. Make a presentation of your ideas to the rest of the group.

Using all your intelligences

The plan for The Weekend Away

Learning in different ways

CHALLENGE

**To learn these verses from
William Blake's poem 'The Tyger'**

*Tyger, tyger burning bright
In the forests of the night,
What immortal hand or eye
Could frame thy fearful symmetry?*

*In what distant deeps or skies
Burnt the fire of thine eyes?
On what wings dare he aspire?
What the hand dare seize the fire?*

*When the stars threw down their spears,
And watered heaven with their tears,
Did he smile his work to see?
Did he who made the Lamb make thee?*

Reproduced with permission of Harper Collins

Working with your best intelligence in
pairs or groups of others with the same
'best' intelligence, learn this quotation.
Use some of the following techniques.

If you are:	
People Smart	Teach each other/test each other, talk about what it means.
Body Smart	Act out the words with actions and mime as you learn it.
Self Smart	Learn it in your head, think about the meaning.
Number Smart	Count the syllables in each line and number the lines. Learn one line at a time with its number.
Word Smart	Find out what each word means and what the story is about. Say the words over and over again out loud.
Picture Smart	Doodle and draw as you say the words. Find a picture to help you remember each line.
Music Smart	Make this into a rap or set it to a musical tune of your choice as you learn it.

Each group perform to the rest of the class to see how well you learnt the passage.

Learn spellings, maths rules, French or German
vocabulary, important dates and people, science words,
phone numbers – learn them using your intelligences.

**Try to use as many
of these intelligences
as you can whenever
you learn.**

Challenging your brain to use the Smarts

Making the Smarts work for you to make you smarter in all subjects

First thoughts

Fill in this timeline to show how you have grown your intelligence since you were a baby. Put key points when you think you may have grown your brain such as talking, walking, learning to ride a bike, read and so on.

Age 1
year ———————————————————————➤

Now add which intelligence you were developing at that time and colour code them.

MULTIPLE INTELLIGENCES – how are you smart?

Now you know what your strengths are, learn to use them to make yourself a genius!

List your 5 strongest intelligences here.	List your favourite subjects here.
1.	1.
2.	2.
3.	3.
4.	4.
5.	5.

Do you always tend to spend time and energy on these favourites?
If you do this it will make them stronger.

List your 3 weakest intelligences here.	List the subjects you find hardest here.
1.	1.
2.	2.
3.	3.

Challenging your brain to use the Smarts

Are you working hard to improve your weak spots? This is the way to improve your brain power.

To maximise your brain power you need to use your strongest intelligences for learning AND improve your weak spots.

Show how could you use your strongest intelligence to help you with your weak spots.

Here is an example:

What I need to work on ↓	Using my No 1 Intelligence BODY SMART I will ...	Using my No 2 Intelligence MUSIC SMART I will ...	Using my No 3 Intelligence PEOPLE SMART I will ...
Number smart	Use cards, beads, fingers to help	Make equations into a rap	Teach your friends formulas
Self smart	Start a fitness training programme and learn to set personal, achievable goals	Use music to create your mood and encourage you to think	Ask friends to give you honest opinions about yourself
Word smart	Learn spellings by tracing out the word on the back of your hand	Listen carefully to the lyrics of songs and find out what they mean	Learn new words from friends who are clever with language

NOW TRY COMPLETING THIS TABLE WITH YOUR OWN IDEAS:

What I need to work on ↓	No 1 intelligence	No 2 intelligence	No 3 intelligence

TASK

Create a television chat show or a newspaper article called

INTELLIGENCE – WHAT'S IT ALL ABOUT ANYWAY?

Challenging your brain to use the Smarts

Intelligence - What's it all about anyway?

_____

_____

_____

_____

_____

_____

_____

_____

_____

_____

_____

_____

_____

_____

_____

_____

_____

_____

_____

_____

_____

_____

Challenging your brain to use the Smarts

Values for
Success in Life

What are the values for success in life?

VALUES – we all need them to be happy and live a life to be proud of

'Human values give respect to life and enhance happiness' *Human Values Foundation*

Values – such as honesty, kindness, love and forgiveness – can determine your behaviour and attitude. Have you thought about YOUR values?

First thoughts

What do you value?

Whom do you value?

What does our country value?

What do you believe in?

Values quiz – rate yourself 1–5 on each of these questions.

1 means you rate yourself low, 5 means very high.

1. I know what my values are.

2. My values help me decide what to do when I have problems.

3. I have opinions on most things.

4. I know what I want in life.

5. I know what my school values.

6. If someone asks me to do something that I don't feel is right, I say no.

Where do you get your values from?

What are the values for success in life?

Here are some values we are going to think about.

 V – Vote for democracy and equality

 A – Attitude is everything

 L – Love is all you need

 U – Understanding that family and friends matter!

 **E** – Enterprise and energy will make you successful

 S – Social intelligence – communicate with confidence

 for

 L – Laughter and fun

 I – I can choose

 **F** – Forgiveness and Fairness

 E – Earn respect through Empathy

TASK

Copy out the box above and create a picture or a different logo to go with each.

What are the values for success in life?

What are the values for success in life?

Telling your story (in pairs)

Tell your story or life history and try to show where your values have come from. Your partner now has to use what they learned in your story and repeat to the class what your key values are and why you have them.

Values for Life

V is for Vote

Values for Success in Life – Vote for democracy and equality

First thoughts

What does democracy mean?

Think of 3 words that sum up democracy for you.

Make a list of everything you have ever voted for, from television shows to school elections.

Voting quiz

At what age can you vote in a local election?

_____

At what age can you vote in a general election?

_____

At what age can you vote in a TV poll?

_____

How did the Prime Minister get his job?

_____

Can you name any countries that don't vote for their leaders?

_____

Would you like to live in one of these countries? Why?

_____

V is for Vote

TASK

What happens ... you decide!

Using the following list, complete Task 1 and Task 2.

TASK 1

Choose your top 6 priorities.

TASK 2

You have £1,000,000.

Assign it to your six priorities. Explain your decision to the class.

Activity	Order of priority	Amount (£)
Nuclear weapons		
New hospitals		
Computers for schools		
Bus services		
Funding for Africa		
Flood defences		
Road tolls		
Prison places		
Youth centres		
Free travel for under 16s		
Cancer Research Funds		
Higher Pensions		
Support for drug addicts		
More parks in cities		

V is for Vote

Can you now complete this sentence?

I should vote because

_____

_____

_____

_____

_____

_____

_____

_____

_____

_____

_____

_____

_____

_____

_____

_____

_____

DEMOCRACY

Extension task

**Is democracy always good?
Does democracy always
mean equality?**

A is for Attitude

Values for Success in Life – Attitude is everything

First thoughts

What do we mean by a bad attitude?

Am I bovvered?

What does it matter what YOU think?

Whatever!

I really don't care!

What's your problem?

A is for Attitude

Discuss the sort of situations when you think or say these statements. What messages are you giving? Why do teenagers act like this?

TASK

Redraw the bubbles with the OPPOSITE view inside them. Colour them in bright colours and draw an appropriate cartoon character.

Employers always stress the importance of attitude for success and career progression. What is a good attitude?

Reference written about an employee who works at a retail store.

Kevin has an attitude problem that affects everything he does and says. He has an unpleasant growl when spoken to and shrugs his shoulders when a customer asks for help. He often just doesn't take advice about how to do the job more effectively and doesn't seem to be listening even when being given important instructions on Health and Safety. He speaks only when spoken to and none of the team wants to work with him. I have had no alternative but to ask him to leave the business.

A is for Attitude

Write the job reference out again saying the opposite of all the comments that have been given about Kevin, thus describing someone with a very positive attitude.

What is your attitude – mark yourself 1–5 (1 is low, 5 is high)

I smile a lot

I greet people in the morning even if I don't know them well

I listen to other's views

I like to do a job well

I don't mind working hard

I like to impress people

I open doors for people or help them out

People who come into contact with me go away feeling happier

I am friendly to people I don't know

I try to use my initiative if I am stuck

I think it's important to keep learning

I am open to new ideas

Faking it to make it

Thinking about what you put into the table above, write yourself a letter of application to get your dream job. Really exaggerate your positive attitude. Work the sentences in the table above into your letter.

A is for Attitude

Letter of application

_____

_____

_____

_____

_____

_____

_____

_____

_____

_____

_____

_____

_____

_____

_____

_____

_____

_____

L is for Love

Values for Success in Life – Love is all you need

What is love?

'Love is an energy which flows from one to another… It is pure, giving and an unselfish experience. It is unconditional' *Human Values Foundation*

Love changes everything … Money can't buy you love …

First thoughts

What does love mean to you?

I love football

I love you

I love chocolate

I love the beach

I love my mum

I love my mates

I love God

I love myself

Discuss the different types of love.

Artists, poets and musicians have always been fascinated by love…

'Love is not love that alters when it alteration finds' (Shakespeare)

'Love means never having to say you're sorry' (tagline from the film Love Story – 1970)

'All you need is love' (The Beatles)

Play some music with lyrics about love and read a selection of love poems.

Complete these sentences to show you can see the different types of love:

Love is _____

Love is _____

Love is _____

Love is _____

Love is _____

Love is _____

L is for Love

What does love feel like, look and sound like?

Do animals love?

Circle the 15 words that relate the most to love for you.

Exciting

Nervous

Soft

Red

Gentle

Dangerous

Black

Angry

Warm

Cold

Shivery

Kind

Worry

Generous

Selfless

Selfish

Blue

Happy

Yellow

Kind

Forgiving

Sorry

Sunshine

Resentful

Happy

Beauty

Safe

Fun

Responsibility

Hope

L is for Love

TASK

What things do you do that demonstrate love?

Is love a value that you would like to include in your top three? Why? Why not?

Task: Imagine an alien from another planet wants you to explain what is meant by love and why it is important to us here on Earth.

Write your explanation:

U is for Understanding

Values for Success in Life – Understanding that family and friends matter!

First thoughts

How has your family influenced you?

How do your friends influence you?

Are there any areas of conflict between friends and family?

Which of the following qualities do you most appreciate in friends and family?

Loyalty	Discipline	Good looks	Cleverness	Coolness
Sense of humour	Generosity	Good listener	Musicality	Popularity
Time for you	Strength	Rich	Optimistic	Love

For family write out the words in red. For friends write out the words in blue.

Use both colours if these qualities are important for both family and friends.

Family	Friends

U is for Understanding

Write an advert for a best friend.

A friend that would make you happy and successful.

What qualities would he or she have?

Wanted: Best friend… 'must…

Wanted: Best friend

U is for Understanding

How can you be a better friend?
Write down five things you can do today.

How do you handle it when you fall out with someone?

Write a list of things families and friends fall out about.

Family   **Friends**

Golden Rules.

Create 5 golden rules for family harmony.

1. _____
2. _____
3. _____
4. _____
5. _____

Create 5 golden rules for friendship.

1. _____
2. _____
3. _____
4. _____
5. _____

Choose one of these examples.
Role-play the conflict and show two versions – a positive and negative outcome.

E is for Enterprise and Energy

Values for Success in Life – Enterprise and Energy

First thoughts

Think of three famous people who have enterprise and energy. Name them.

Enterprise means you are not scared to take a risk – you have courage and a willingness to do a difficult task – and can think of new and original solutions. You take the initiative; you do not wait for someone else to go first.

Energy means you are lively and enthusiastic about working hard for what you want.

What is the opposite of these?

Why will having both enterprise *and* energy make you unstoppable?

TASK

Dragon's Den

Vote for the 3–5 most enterprising and energetic people in the class to be the Dragons. The Dragons will work out their imaginary careers and prepare criteria for how they will judge each group's products.

In groups, invent a product to sell to the Dragons. (20 mins.)

Each Dragon has up to £50,000 to invest in each group.

Prepare a 3 minute presentation to make to the Dragons that will convince them to invest in your group.

The winning group will be the one that attracts the most investment.

The Dragons have to give positive feedback on how to be enterprising and energetic to all groups.

Extension task

Create a mini business that will raise money for your favourite charity.

E is for Enterprise and Energy

My Mini Business

S is for Social intelligence

Values for Success in Life – Social intelligence

How to be popular, feel confident with people and be a great communicator

Getting on with people – often called interpersonal intelligence – is one of the most important skills for life. However, much of what we do when we communicate is not in our conscious awareness and we may not realise the impression we are making on others.

First thoughts

When you first meet someone what do you notice about them?

How long does it take you to form an opinion about whether you like them or not?

What impression do YOU make? There are some people that are immediately likeable. So **how would you make sure that you are one.**

The chart below shows what is important about you to the person you are communicating to:

Vocal: HOW YOU SOUND. 38%
Volume, pitch, pace, intonation and energy

Visual: THE WAY YOU LOOK. 55%
Posture, gestures, facial expressions, eye contact and dress

Content: WHAT YOU SAY. Only 7%

Make the above into a diagram, pie chart or cartoon.

S is for Social intelligence

So **body language** matters more than what you say. Body language is made up of:

1.   Your facial expressions.

2.   How you stand or sit.

3.   Whether you can keep eye contact.

4.   Posture and gesture.

5.   How you shake hands.

Your body language is very important in making you feel confident.

Think of someone who is confident. Describe their body language. Draw some stick men to show confident and anxious body posture. Draw some facial expressions too.

S is for Social intelligence

Volunteer to walk into the room with anxious and confident body language and see how it makes you feel. What do other people recognise in your body language?

The way you walk and talk can make you feel differently too. When you feel worried you could change the way you feel by walking like your hero.

Positive body language also helps you get rapport with people you meet.

> Getting rapport is the key to making a great impact and being a confident communicator when you meet people.
>
> Rapport is 'a harmonious or sympathetic connection' with someone else. If you can get this then you will always make a good impression. To get rapport you need to 'tune' in to what others need and feel. Friends do this automatically. They match and mirror each other's behaviour and body language so that they feel comfortable with each other.

Talk in pairs about a holiday you would love to go on. Try to mirror each other's movements in a natural way and see how it feels.

TASK

Write out the actions from the list below that you think would help you get rapport.

Smile	Tilt your head sideways	Fold your arms	Turn your back	Slouch
Keep eye contact	Shoulders back	Frown	Raise your eyes to heaven	Speak clearly
Look down	Have your hair flop in your eyes	Head up	Laugh	Tut

TASK

Sell your pen to your neighbour – use rapport and mirroring to get rapport with your customer.

How did you describe it?

How much did you sell it for?

> **TOP TIP:** From now on think about how you impact on others. Practise getting and breaking rapport and ask for feedback from people about how you come across to them.

S is for Social intelligence

L is for Laughter and fun

Values for Success in Life – Laughter and fun

First thoughts

Discuss your favourite comedy programmes and comedians. How do they make you laugh? Do they exaggerate body language?

How often do you laugh? When was the last time and what caused it? Discuss with your neighbour.

LAUGHTER CHANGES YOUR BRAIN – try it. Make yourself laugh out loud and you will find it is contagious and you **really** will begin to laugh. This sparks the production of chemicals called endorphins in your brain that make you feel good.

What or who makes you laugh?

How do you make others laugh?

Why do some people laugh more often than others?

Can you laugh at yourself?

Why does alcohol make people giggle?

Being able to laugh at yourself is a powerful way to boost your confidence and self-esteem because it enables you to laugh at mistakes and move forward.

L is for Laughter and fun

List some of your own and your family's funniest habits and share them with the group.

Can you make fun and laughter an important value in your life?

Tell a (clean) funny story to your neighbour – it can be made up or real.

In a group, share some jokes, and then analyse why they are funny.

Why do these things make us laugh?

★ Exaggeration
★ Falling over
★ Tickling
★ Teasing
★ Tricking others
★ Mistakes

L is for Laughter and fun

How do you feel when others laugh **at** you?

How can you make others laugh **with** you?

A teenager wrote the letter below to the problem page of a magazine.
Write a reply giving good advice on how to deal with the problems in future.

> Dear Jimbo,
>   Every time I'm out with my mates
> I seem to say something stupid and
> everyone laughs at me.
>   I've started to just keep quiet but
> some of them still make fun of me
> and I just don't know how to react.
> Help!!
>   Yours...
>   'Depressed'

Everybody loves a joker – or do they?

What does your neighbour think of the advice you gave and why?

Think of the jokes you know.

How many are hurtful in some way?

TOP TIPS: for getting **real** laughter into your life:
- Tell a joke which isn't hurtful
- Smile at someone today – make them feel good
- Make sure you laugh *with* people not *at* them
- Don't take yourself too seriously
- See the funny side of mistakes you make

I is for I can choose

Values for Success in Life – I can choose

This value is about your own personal power:

The power to forgive, the power to choose, the power to be happy, the power to manage your mind, the power to communicate…

But with power comes responsibility. Your greatest responsibility is to yourself.

First thoughts

Who influences you?

Peer group pressure

How good are you at doing what *you* want?

Rate yourself (honestly) on how much you would be influenced by what others in your peer group think of the following:

Give yourself 1 for very low influence and 5 for very high influence	
1. The clothes you buy	
2. The music you listen to	
3. The friends you have	
4. Your hobbies and interests	
5. The lessons you like	
6. How hard you work at school	
7. The teachers you get on with	
8. Your attitude to your parents	
9. Your career ambitions	
10. How you spend your free time	
Total	**/ 50**

⬛ is for ⬛ can choose

Who is in control of your life?

How can peer groups influence you in negative ways?

How can you be strong and stick to your values?

How many of your friends will still be your friends in ten years' time?
Describe the qualities of the friends who will still be around.

Create a group role-play that shows a group planning to commit a crime.
Show how members of the group can influence each other to do
things they would never do alone.

If it's to be it's up to me

I is for I can choose

Write down the 5s:

Write down five excuses for not doing your homework:

1. _____
2. _____
3. _____
4. _____
5. _____

Write down five excuses for not tidying your room:

1. _____
2. _____
3. _____
4. _____
5. _____

Write down five things you want in life:

1. _____
2. _____
3. _____
4. _____
5. _____

Write down five excuses for not getting them:

1. _____
2. _____
3. _____
4. _____
5. _____

Personal power means taking responsibility.
No excuses. No blaming others.
Just know you can make great choices.

'I CAN CHOOSE' – say that to yourself every day.

F is for Forgiveness and Fairnesss

Values for Success in Life – Forgiveness and Fairness

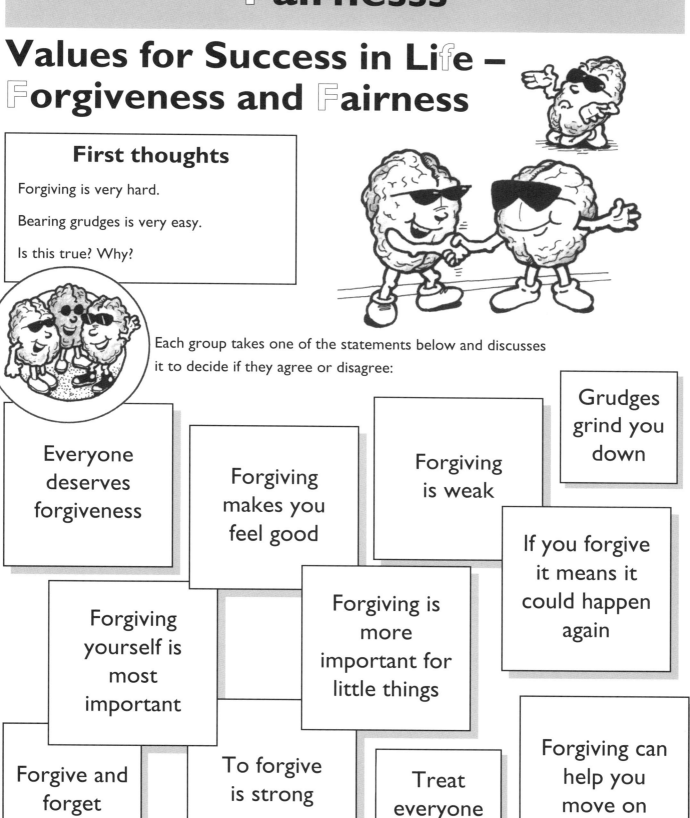

First thoughts

Forgiving is very hard.

Bearing grudges is very easy.

Is this true? Why?

Each group takes one of the statements below and discusses it to decide if they agree or disagree:

Everyone deserves forgiveness

Forgiving makes you feel good

Forgiving is weak

Grudges grind you down

If you forgive it means it could happen again

Forgiving yourself is most important

Forgiving is more important for little things

Forgive and forget

To forgive is strong

Treat everyone equally

Forgiving can help you move on

F is for Forgiveness and Fairness

Share what your group thought with the class.

What happens when you can't forgive and you bear a grudge? How do you feel? List your emotions.

Make up six questions about forgiveness such as:

How does it feel to forgive?

Why should I forgive?

1. _____
2. _____
3. _____
4. _____
5. _____
6. _____

Think of a real story about something that happened that made you feel angry. Write it down or tell it to your neighbour. Now answer each of your six questions and relate it to your story.

1. _____
2. _____
3. _____
4. _____
5. _____
6. _____

F is for Forgiveness and Fairness

Being fair means being able to weigh up what is right and wrong and to make a good decision.

You can't change what has happened but you can change how you feel about it.

Grudge is small and mean and angry.

Forgiveness is big and generous and kind.

Forgiveness and fairness go together.

'People will forget what you say, people will forget what you do but people will never forget how you made them feel.'

Is it fair that the food that you throw away in your bin could feed the starving families of Africa?

Can those families forgive you for throwing that good food away?

Extension task

Look up Fair Trade on the Internet and see what it means.

Hold a Community of Enquiry discussion in a circle about 'fairness'.

E is for Earn respect through Empathy

Values for Success in Life – Earn respect through Empathy

Develop empathy to earn respect.

Empathy is the ability to put yourself into someone else's shoes. Empathy creates RESPECT for yourself and those around you.

First thoughts

Think of three people you respect and write their names below. Why do you respect them?

1 _____ 2 _____ 3 _____

_____ _____ _____

_____ _____ _____

_____ _____ _____

What actions make you respect yourself?

_____

_____

What actions make you respect someone else?

_____

_____

How can you earn respect from your friends?

_____

_____

E is for Earn respect through Empathy

er pressure

Don't speak to him, no one likes him 'cos he's too boffy...

You've got to have one of these - we all do...

Haven't you got a boyfriend yet?

Will they still like me if I don't stand up to him?

Make up some more thought bubbles or speech bubbles that represent the dilemmas of self-respect versus group-respect.

hat's the difference?

ood manners	Self-respect	Respect from others	Being polite

TASK

Create a personal shield that shows what respect means to you using pictures and words. Show your shield to the class and describe what it means.

VALUES Review task

Democracy and equality   Social communication

Attitude   Laughter and fun

Love   Personal responsibility

Friends and family   Forgiveness and fairness

Enterprise and energy   Empathy and respect

From the ten VALUES you have discussed, choose your top five and create a logo around your name or nickname that weaves those values around you. Copy it and stick it on your books and belongings.

E is for Earn respect through Empathy

My personal shield.

Crown House Publishing Limited
www.crownhouse.co.uk – www.chpus.com
Illustration Les Evans

ISBN 978-184590103-5
9 781845 901035
9 00

The Learner's Toolkit

Workbook 2

Lessons in Learning to Learn
Values for Success in Life

Name:

Jackie Beere

Edited by Ian Gilbert

First published by

Crown House Publishing Ltd
Crown Buildings, Bancyfelin, Carmarthen, Wales, SA33 5ND, UK
www.crownhouse.co.uk

and

Crown House Publishing Company LLC
6 Trowbridge Drive, Suite 5, Bethel, CT 06801, USA
www.chpus.com

First published 2008. Reprinted 2008.

British Library of Cataloguing-in-Publication Data
A catalogue entry for this book is available from the British Library.

13-digit ISBN 978-184590103-5

The author and publisher gratefully acknowledge the permission granted to reproduce the copyright material in this book.

'The Tyger' by William Blake has been reproduced with the permission of Harper Collins.

Every effort has been made to trace copyright holders and to obtain their permission for the use of copyright material. The publisher apologises for any errors or omissions and would be grateful if they could be notified of any corrections that should be incorporated in future reprints or editions of this book.

Edited by Ian Gilbert.